To Annabel and Evie,
Many Blessings and Love
GOD is always with you.
Cynthia Goodwin Smith

Where Is God?

By Cynthia Goodwin Smith
Illustrated by Wanda Grice

Where Is God?
By Cynthia Goodwin Smith
Illustrated by Wanda Grice

To Jesus Christ,

My savior and yours,

And children everywhere,

Especially the young at heart.

With love to my husband, Erich; daughter, Kristin;

and grandchildren, Lary, Ellie, Sawyer, Katie, Bailey,

and Erich, who was the inspiration for this book.

Where is God?

But if from there you seek the Lord your God, you will find him if you seek him with all your heart and with all your soul. — Deuteronomy 4:29

I AM Here

I AM the Alpha and the Omega, the First and the Last,
the Beginning and the End. — Revelation 22:13

I AM like a tree that gives you shade.

Blessed is the one who trusts in the Lord, whose confidence is in him. They will be like a tree planted by the water that sends out its roots by the stream.
— Jeremiah 17:7–8

I AM like the moon that lights your way.

"I am the light of the world. Whoever follows me will never walk in darkness, but will have the light of life."
— John 8:12

I AM like your blanket, cozy and warm,

The Lord wraps himself in light as with a garment; he stretches out the heavens like a tent. — Psalm 104:2

Giving you hugs, all the day long.

As a mother comforts her child,
so will I comfort you. — Isaiah 66:13

I AM like a hand reaching out in the night,

For I am the Lord your God, who takes hold
of your right hand and says to you,
Do not fear; I will help you. — Isaiah 41:13

Like a friend in a storm,

Each one will be like a shelter from the wind and a refuge from the storm. — Isaiah 32:2

Saying, "Hold on tight!"

I cling to you; your right hand
upholds me. — Psalm 63:8

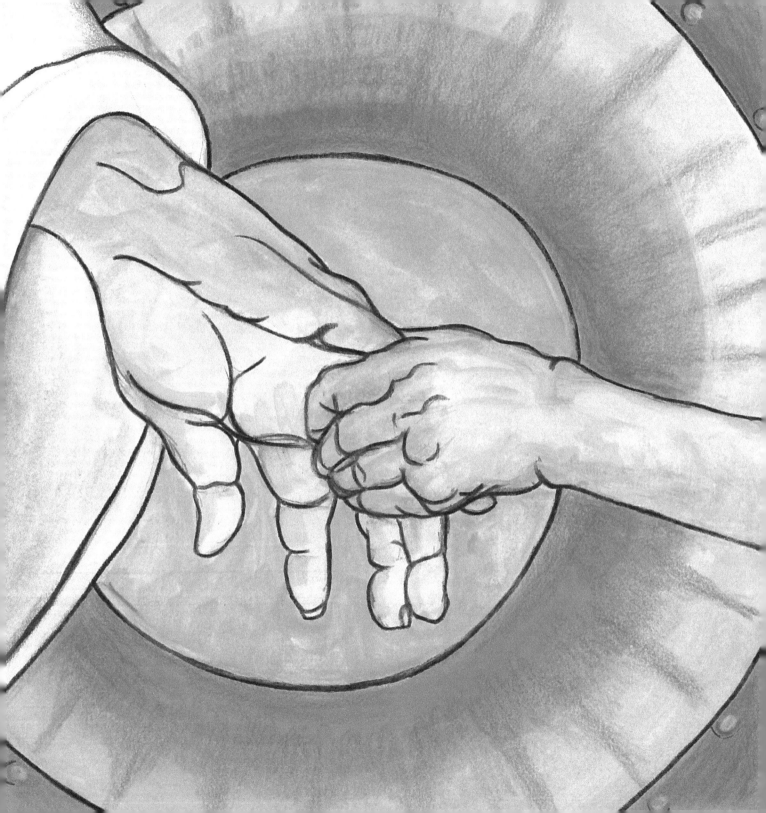

Through the wind and waves and their tossing about,

For I Am the Lord your God, who churns up the sea
so that its waves roar—the Lord Almighty
is his name. — Isaiah 51:15

I AM within and I am about.

"I am in my Father, and you are in me,
and I am in you." —John 14:20

I AM here
with you now.
You are not without.

Now we see only a reflection as in a mirror;
then we shall see face to face. — 1 Corinthians 13:12

Just hold on; grab my hand, and together you steady yourselves!

Keep my steps steady according
to your promise. — Psalm 119:133 NRS

I AM here, always here — throughout!

"Surely I am with you always,
to the very end of the age." — Matthew 28:20

Tossing and Turning at times we will go, Playing catch to and fro.

For the eyes of the Lord run to and fro throughout the whole earth, to show himself strong on behalf of those whose heart is loyal to him. — 2 Chronicles 16:9 NKJV

No matter what, I want you to know,

"I am the way and the truth and the life. No one comes to the Father except through me." — John 14:6

I AM deep in your heart forever, you know.

Do not let your hearts be troubled, believe in God, believe also in me." — John 14:1 NRSV 6

I AM GOD STATEMENTS

I AM your shield, your very great reward." — Genesis 15:1

I AM God Almighty, walk before me faithfully and be blameless. — Genesis 17:1

I AM with you and will watch over you wherever you go. — Genesis 28:15

I AM who I AM. — Exodus 3:14

Be still and know that I AM God." — Psalm 46:10

Do not fear, for I AM with you, do not be afraid for I AM your God. — Isaiah 41:10

I AM the Lord, the God of all mankind. Is anything too hard for me? — Jeremiah 32:27

"I AM with you always, to the end of the age." — Matthew 28:20. NRSV

"I AM the bread of life." — John 6:35

"I AM the light of the world."— John 8:12

"I AM the gate; whoever enters through me will be saved. He will come in, go out and find pasture." — John 10:9

"I AM the good shepherd. The good shepherd lays down his life for the sheep." — John 10:11

"I AM the way and the truth and the life." — John 14:6

"I AM in my father and you are in me and I AM in you." — John 14:10

"I AM the vine and my father is the true gardener. " — John 15:1

"I AM the Alpha and the Omega," says the Lord God, "who is and who was and who is to come, the Almighty." — Revelation 1:8

"Yes, I AM coming soon." Amen. Come, Lord Jesus. — Revelation 22:20

About the Author

Cynthia Goodwin Smith
Win Today. Win Tomorrow. Win for Life.
Website: TheGoodWin.co

Cynthia Goodwin Smith holds BS and MS degrees in Social Work and is a Licensed Clinical Social Worker with 25 years' experience. She worked as a therapist with at-risk children and their families, and as a Case Manager for a Mental Health Provider. She authored several articles for her company's newsletter. She also has over 15 years' experience as a personal life coach for women teaching them to identify, express, and achieve their inner most desires, goals, dreams, and aspirations. Cynthia is a prayer team leader at her church where she authored a Lenten daily devotional titled "Living Water." For the past five years, she has been a Pastoral Care Volunteer at a major Medical and Trauma Center.

While reading to her grandson one day, he asked 'Where is God?' This compelled her to apply her experience, and with God's help, authored her first book to help children and their parents answer this meaningful question.

About the Illustrator

Wanda Grice
WandARTful Glory
Email: **gricewanda@gmail.com**

Wanda Grice a West Texas native, who moved to the Dallas-Fort Worth area fulfilling a dream. She traded crayons for pastels, finger paint for acrylics, and construction paper for canvas. Her calling is to create WandARTful Glory from uncommon objects, allowing the viewer to experience an Artistic Realm Transformation.

She has created works in watercolor and mixed media. She is currently working in acrylics. Her most recent works have been religiously inspired and focused. She is an artist and award nominated illustrator. She is a active member and board member of several local arts groups and participates regularly at her home church.

CPSIA information can be obtained
at www.ICGtesting.com
Printed in the USA
LVHW020815300819
629322LV00002B/7/P

9 780578 435657